Book © 1991 CPP/BELWIN, INC.
15800 N.W. 48th Avenue, Miami, Florida 33014

Editor: Carol Cuellar

CONTENTS

MUSTANG SALLY

Words and Music by
BONNY RICE

Moderate rock ♩ = 120

Mus-tang Sal-

Verse:

ly,   guess you bet-ter slow that Mus-tang   down.—

—   Mus-tang

Sal-ly, now ba - by,   guess you bet-ter slow that Mus-tang   down.—

Mustang Sally - 4 - 1
P0935SMX

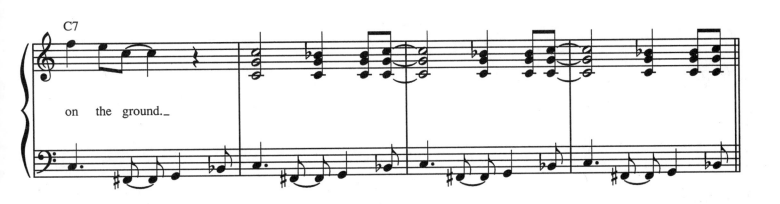

Chorus:

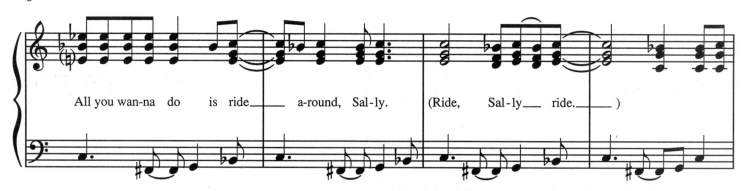

All you wan-na do is ride____ a-round, Sal-ly. (Ride, Sal-ly__ ride.__)

All you wan-na do is ride____ a-round,__ Sal-ly. (Ride, Sal-ly__ ride.

__) All you wan-na do is ride____ a-round, Sal-ly.

(Ride, Sal-ly,__ ride.__) One of these ear-ly morn-

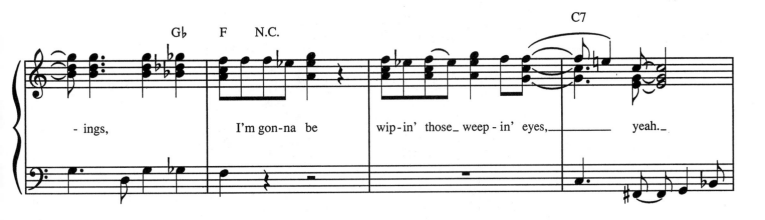

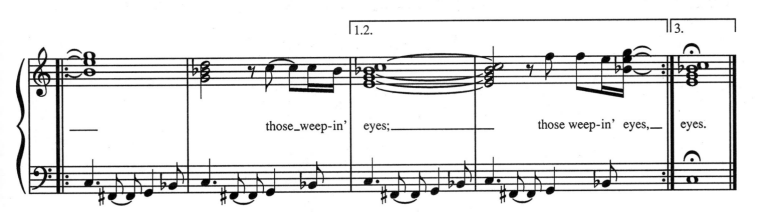

Verse 2:
I bought you a brand new Mustang,
It was a nineteen sixty five.
Now you come around, signifying a woman.
Girl, you won't, you won't let me ride.
Mustang Sally, now baby,
Guess you better slow that Mustang down.
You been runnin' all over town.
Oh, guess you gotta put your flat feet on the ground.
(To Chorus:)

CHAIN OF FOOLS

Words and Music by
DON COVAY

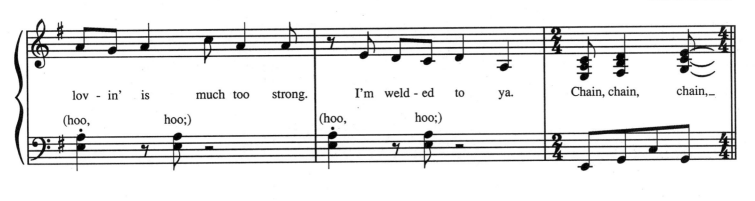

lov-in' is   much too strong.   I'm weld-ed to   ya.   Chain, chain,   chain,_
(hoo,   hoo;)   (hoo,   hoo;)

Coda

Chain, chain, chain,_   Chain, chain, chain,

Chain, chain, chain,_____ yeah,   chain of fools._

Chain, chain, chain,_   Chain, chain, chain._

Verse 2:
One of these mornings that chain is gonna break.
But up until then, I'm gonna take all I can take.
(To Coda)

DESTINATION ANYWHERE

Words and Music by
NICKOLAS ASHFORD and VALERIE SIMPSON

1. Said to the man at the rail-road sta-tion, "I want a tick-et, just____ ____ one."____ He said, "Well,____ if you in sist.____

Chorus:

Where you wan-na go, Miss?"____ Oh,____ des-ti-na-tion, an-

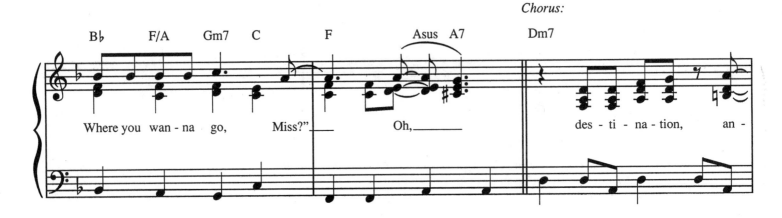

Destination Anywhere - 4 - 1
P0935SMX

14

Verse 3:
As I stared through the window of the train,
I thought I heard my baby call my name.
But it was just the conductor saying,
"Which stop would you prefer?"
(To Chorus:)

I CAN'T STAND THE RAIN

Words and Music by
DON BRYANT, ANN PEEBLES
and BERNARD MILLER

Moderate slow rock ♩ = 84

I_____ can't stand the rain_____ a - gainst my

win - dow,_____ you're bring-in' back sweet mem-o-

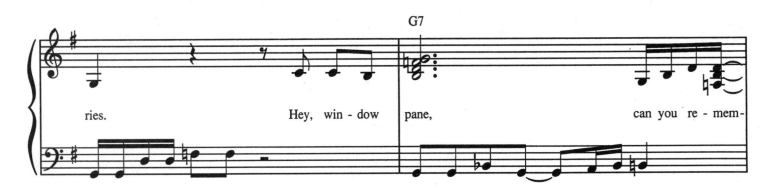

ries. Hey, win - dow pane, can you re - mem-

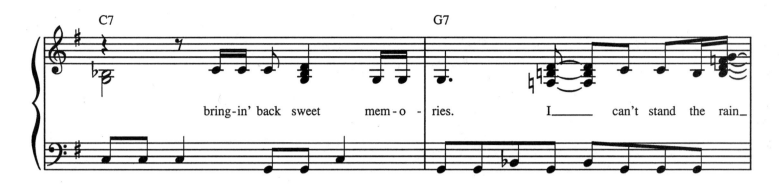

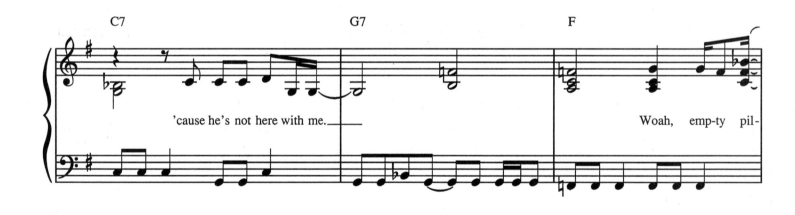

TAKE ME TO THE RIVER

Words and Music by
AL GREEN and MABON HODGES

Take Me to the River - 4 - 1
P0935SMX

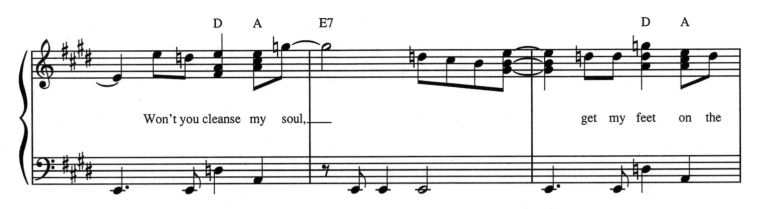

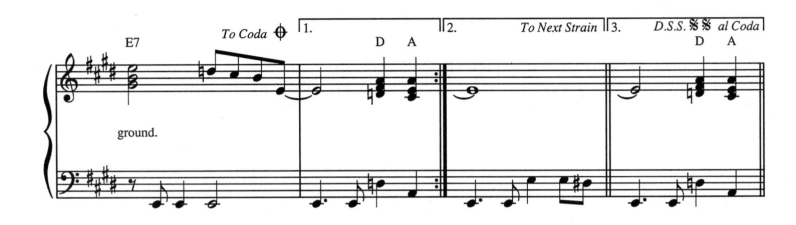

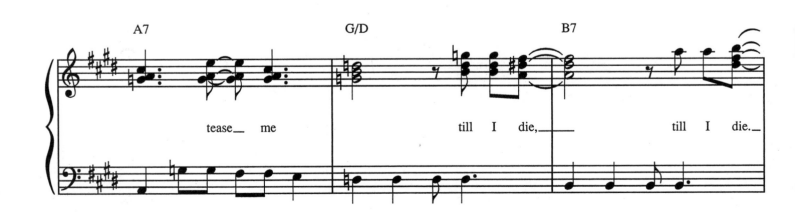

Take Me to the River - 4 - 3
P0935SMX

TRY A LITTLE TENDERNESS

Words and Music by
HARRY WOODS, JIMMY CAMPBELL
and REG. CONNELLY

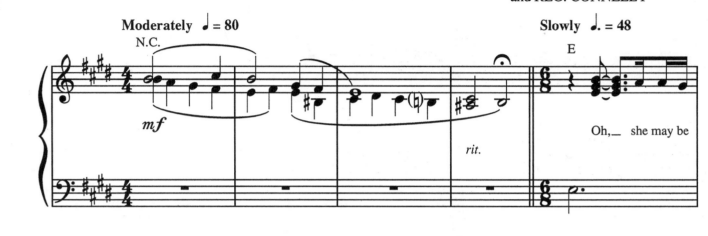

26

so____ eas - y, all you got-ta do is try a lit-tle

ten-der - ness,____ yeah.____

Squeeze her, tease her, nev-er leave her, you got to, you *got to, you got to, you got to* try a lit-tle

ten-der-ness, yeah, yeah.____ ten-der-ness.

rit.

IN THE MIDNIGHT HOUR

Words and Music by
WILSON PICKETT and
STEVE CROPPER

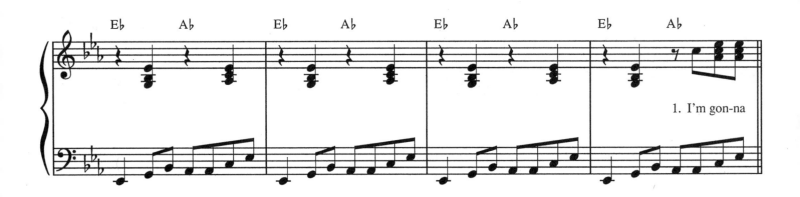

1. I'm gon-na

Verse:

wait till the mid-night hour;_____ that's when my loves comes_ tum-bling down.___

_ I'm gon-na wait till the mid-night hour,_____ when there's

no one___ else a - round.___ I'm gon - na take you, girl,___ and

hold___ you and do all the things I told___ you in the mid-night hour.___

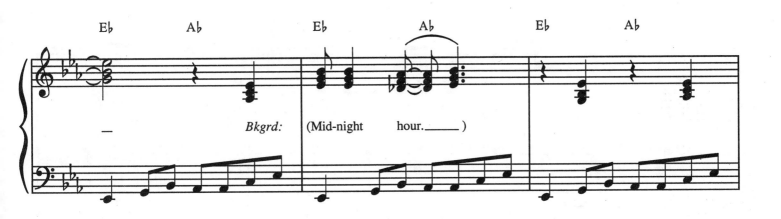

_ *Bkgrd:* (Mid-night hour.___)

2. I'm gon - na

Bridge:

Repeat ad lib. and fade

I'm gon-na wait till the mid-night hour;___
wait till the mid-night hour;___
(Wait,)

___ that's when my love comes_ tumb-ling down.___ I'm gon-na
(mid-night hour.____) that's when my love be-gins to shine.___ I'm gon-na
(mid-night hour.____)

Verse 2:
I'm gonna wait till the stars come out,
And see the twinkle in your eye.
I'm gonna wait till the midnight hour;
That's when my love begins to shine.
You are the only girl I love,
And really loves me so in the midnight hour.
(To Bridge:)

BYE BYE BABY

Words and Music by
MARY WELLS

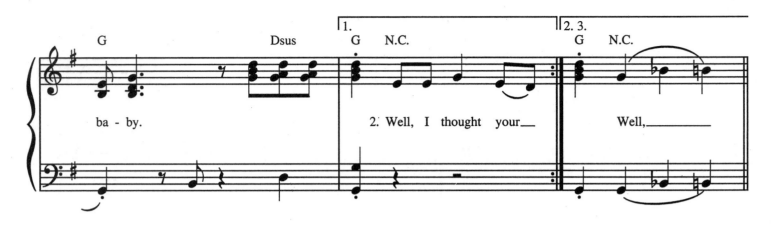

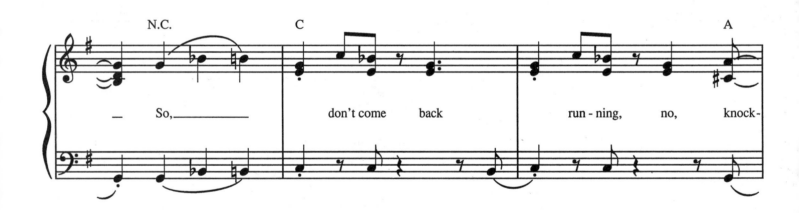

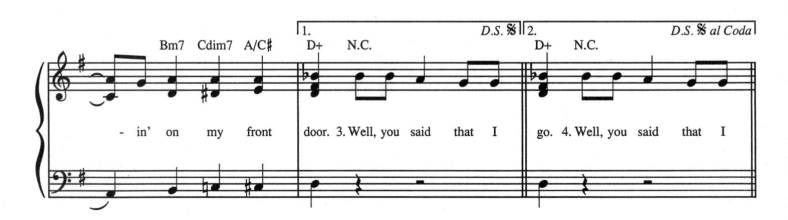

Verse 2:
Well, I thought your love
Was oh so true,
Oh, till you made me baby,
Yeah, start loving you.
You know you took my love, threw it away.
But you're gonna want my love someday,
Well, bye bye baby.
(To Bridge:)

Verse 3:
Well, you said that I
Was your loving girl.
No one, no other
In this whole wide world.
You know you took my love, threw it away,
But you're gonna want my love someday,
Well, bye bye baby.
(To Bridge:)

THE DARK END OF THE STREET

Words and Music by
CHIPS MOMAN and DAN PENN

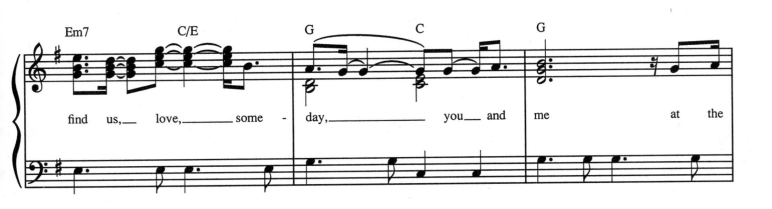

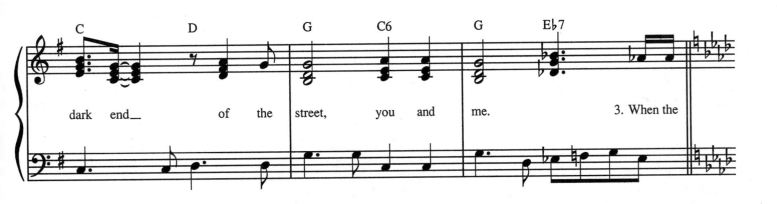

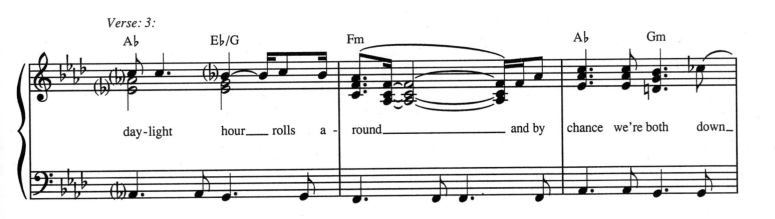

the town, if we should meet_ just walk,_walk on_ by, yeah,_ oh,

dar - ling,_ please don't cry. To-night we meet at the

dark end_ of the street,_ mm.

molto rit.

Verse 2:
I know time is gonna take its toll.
We have to pay for the love we stole.
It's a sin and we know it's wrong,
Oh, but our love, it keeps comin' on strong.
Steal away to the dark end of the street, you and me.
(To Bridge:)

DO RIGHT WOMAN DO RIGHT MAN

Words and Music by
CHIPS MOMAN and DAN PENN

Do Right Woman Do Right Man - 3 - 1
P0935SMX

I NEVER LOVED A MAN

Words and Music by
RONNY SHANNON

I Never Loved a Man - 3 - 2
P0935SMX

Verse 2:
Sometime ago I thought
You'd run out of fuel.
I was so wrong,
'Cause you've got what you'll never lose.
The way you treat me is a shame.
How could you hurt me so bad?
Baby, don't you know
That I'm the best thing you've ever had?

Chorus 2:
Kiss me once again;
Don't you ever never say that we're through,
'Cause I ain't never, (never)
I ain't never, (never)
I ain't never, (never) no, no,
Loved a man
The way that I,
I love you.
(To Bridge:)

MR. PITIFUL

Words and Music by
OTIS REDDING &
STEVE CROPPER

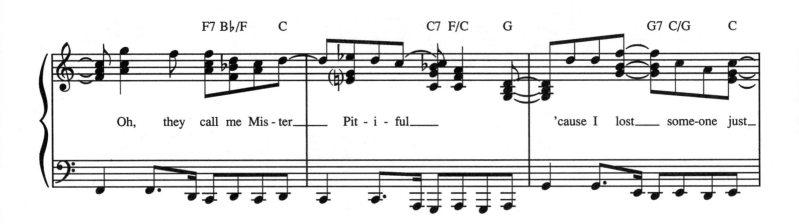

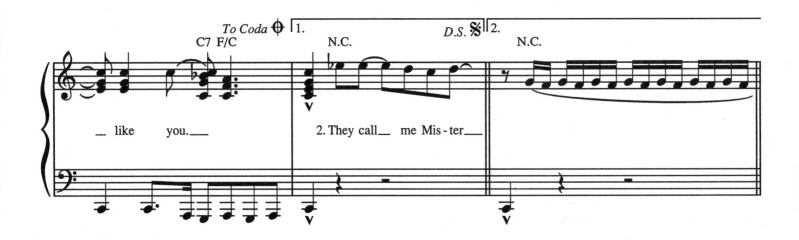

Verse 2:
They call me Mr. Pitiful; yes, everybody knows, now.
They call me Mr. Pitiful most every place I go.
But nobody seems to understand, now, what makes a man sing such a sad song,
When he lost everything, when he lost everything he had.
(To Bridge:)

SLIP AWAY

Words and Music by
WILBUR TERRELL, MARCUS DANIEL
and WILLIAM ARMSTRONG

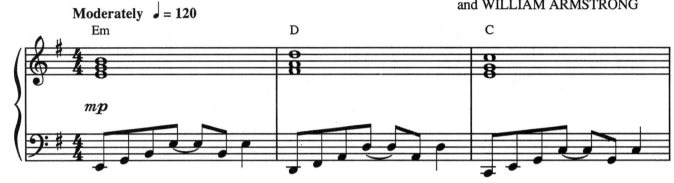

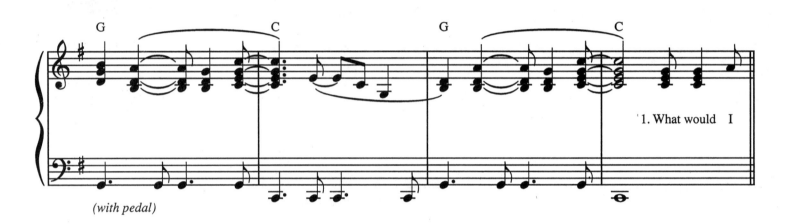

1. What would I

give for just a few_ more min-utes?

What would I give_____ just to have_ you near?_

Slip Away - 3 - 1
P0935SMX

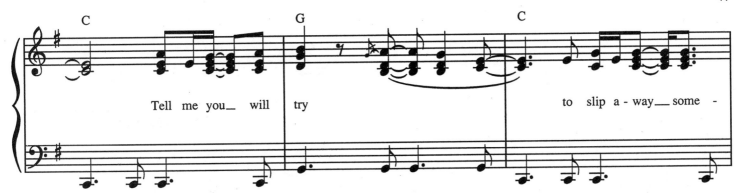

Verse 2:
But I know it's wrong,
The things I ask you to do.
But please believe me, darling,
I don't mean to hurt you.
Could you slip away
Without him knowing you're gone?
Then we can meet somewhere,
Somewhere where we both are not known.
(To Chorus:)

TREAT HER RIGHT

Words and Music by
ROY HEAD and GENE KURTZ

Treat Her Right - 3 - 1
P0935SMX

hey!

Hey, hey, hey, hey!

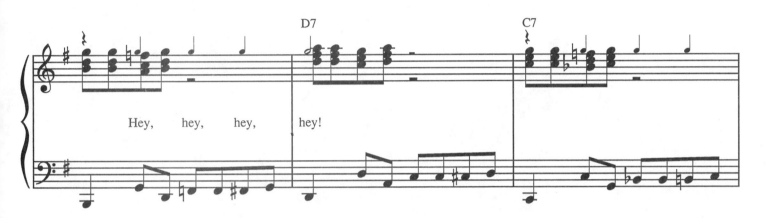

Hey, hey, hey, hey!

4. I wan-na tell you a

Verse 2:
Oh, squeeze her real gentle;
Gotta make her feel good.
Tell her that you love her
Like you know you should.
And you'll be glad every night
That you treated her right.

Verse 3:
If you practice my method
Just as hard as you can,
You're gonna get a reputation
As a lovin' man.
And you'll be glad every night
That you treated her right.
(To Chorus:)

Verse 4:
I wanna tell you a story
Every man oughta know.
If you want a little lovin',
You gotta start real slow.
She's gonna love you tonight
If you just treat her right.

Verse 5:
Oh, squeeze her real gentle;
Gotta make her feel good.
Tell her that you love her
Like you know you should.
'Cause if you don't treat her right,
She won't love you tonight.
(To Chorus:)